Maths We~~~~~
Workout
Year 3

Peter Patilla &
Paul Broadbent

Every effort has been made to trace copyright holders and to obtain their permission for the use of copyright material. The authors and publishers will gladly receive information enabling them to rectify any error or omission in subsequent editions.

First published 2001

Letts Educational,
The Chiswick Centre
414 Chiswick High Rd
London
W4 5TF
Tel: (020) 8996 3333
Fax: (020) 8742 8390

www.letts-education.com

Text © Peter Patilla and Paul Broadbent
Illustrations © Peter and Janet Simmonett.
Cover illustration © Peter and Janet Simmonett.
Editorial, design and production by Gecko Limited, Cambridge

British Library Cataloguing-in-Publication Data
A CIP record for this book is available from the British Library.

ISBN 1 84085 620 3

Printed and bound in the UK.
Letts Educational, a division of Granada Learning Ltd.
Part of Granada Media Group.

CONTENTS

Introduction 4

1 Zap the digit 6

2 Reach the total 7

3 Money match 8

4 Time for it 9

5 Measurement challenge 10

6 Exploding shapes 11

7 The answer is 7 12

8 Steps 13

9 Digit poser 14

10 Coin grid 15

11 Half and half 16

12 Choice subtractions 17

13 Pictogram problem 18

14 Alphabet sums 19

15 Abacus 20

16 Number clues 21

17 Addition squares 22

18 Coin totals 23

19 Two shapes into one 24

20 Make a tocker 25

21 Twenty pence question 26

22 Target jumps 27

23 Domino sums 28

24 Alphabet divisions 29

25 Five-square halves 30

26 Bar graph problem 31

27 Half past three 32

28 Breaking up 33

29 Triangle totals 34

30 Design a stamp book 35

31 Corner totals 36

32 Making spells 37

33 Shape puzzle 38

34 Century answers 39

35 Sorting numbers 40

36 Puzzling remainders 41

37 Matching coins 42

38 Fraction shields 43

39 Measurement words 44

40 Column graph problem 45

41 Decade totals 46

Glossary 47

Maths content 48

INTRODUCTION

Solving problems: how to use this book

Share your ideas with your partner and listen to their ideas.

Write out your rough workings very neatly.

It is your problem. Try not to ask the teacher for help.

After each problem set yourself a challenge.

These are problems so do not give up right away if you become stuck.

Why not make a maths log book that keeps all your problems together?

Why not make a group or class notice-board to show your results?

Why not check your answers with your partner?

Why not write results on Post-it notes? They can be moved and rearranged.

Why not try to find lots of different solutions to each problem?

Why not make a poster to show your results?

Think about working on the problem at home.

Zap the digit

A digit is zapped when it changes to 0.

Here is how to zap 256.

 Enter $-6=$ →  The 6 is zapped.

 Enter $-50=$ →  The 5 is zapped.

 Enter $-200=$ →  The 2 is zapped.

Play this game with a partner.

Each of you enters a hundreds number on a calculator.

Take turns to zap the digits from your partner's display.

The digits can be zapped in any order.

Start with larger numbers.

Turn this into a scoring game.

Zap digits by adding.

6

Reach the total

Choose from these four digits. Use + and =.

What totals can you make?

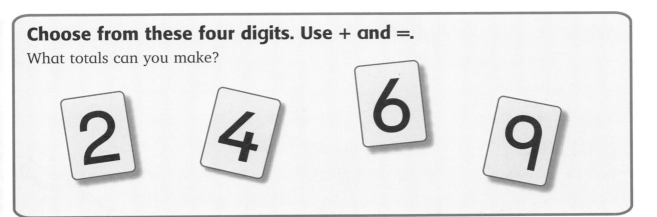

You can make totals of 15 and 30 like this.

Write your totals in order.

Sort your totals into sets.

Choose your own set of four digits.

Money match

Which sets of silver coins
can you use to pay for these?

43p

99p

68p

Here is a **sensible** set for 24p.

24p

Here is a **silly** set for 24p.

24p

Can you see why it is silly?

Write your
sets in order.

Use copper coins
as well as silver
coins.

Choose
your own
price
labels.

8

UNIT 4

Time for it

What can you do in exactly 20 seconds?
Work with a partner and time each other.

Make a poster or table to show what you can do.

Use a different time instead of 20 seconds.

9

Measurement challenge

- Work with a partner. Draw a table like this.

- Take turns to choose two of the points on the diagram below. Estimate how far they are apart in centimetres.

Points chosen	Estimate (cm)	Higher or lower?	Score	
			Player A	Player B

- Your partner says whether they think the measurement is **higher** or **lower** than your estimate.

- Measure to find out.

- If your partner is correct, they score 2. If your partner is wrong, you score 2.

Design your own diagram and play the game again.

Exploding shapes

Here are two exploding shapes. Can you see how they have been made?

Create your own exploding shapes.

Start from squares, triangles and circles.

Use curved cuts as well as straight cuts.

Can you find a way of sorting your exploded shapes?

11

The answer is 7

The answer to a calculation is 7.

What could the calculation be?

Sort the calculations into boxes like this.

Could there be more boxes?

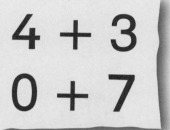

4 + 3
0 + 7

7

20 – 13
22 – 15

What could
be in the
empty box?

Why not use
three numbers in
a calculation?

Why not use
fractions?

12

UNIT 8

Steps

How many steps are there from 4 to 16?

Here is the solution for 4 steps.

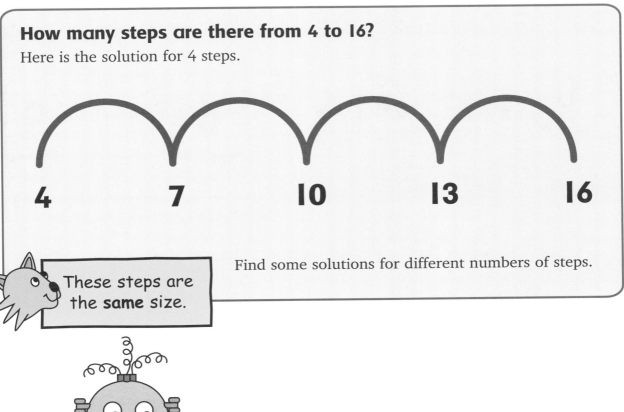

4   7   10   13   16

These steps are the **same** size.

Find some solutions for different numbers of steps.

Make each step a different size.

Choose your own start and finish numbers.

What if you must not step on odd numbers?

13

Digit poser

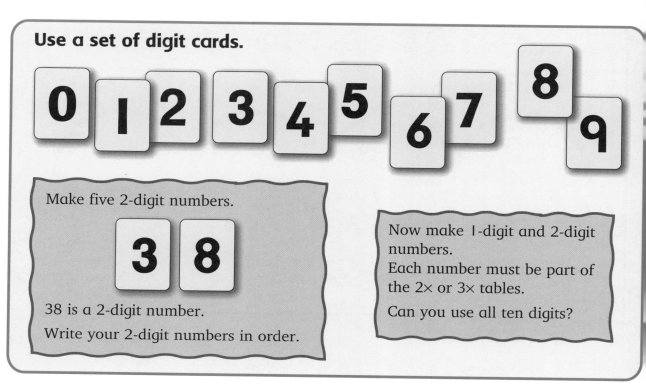

Use a set of digit cards.

0 1 2 3 4 5 6 7 8 9

Make five 2-digit numbers.

3 8

38 is a 2-digit number.

Write your 2-digit numbers in order.

Now make 1-digit and 2-digit numbers.
Each number must be part of the 2× or 3× tables.

Can you use all ten digits?

Make all the numbers even.

Make 2-digit and 3-digit numbers.

Choose your own rule for making sets of numbers.

14

Coin grid

You need these coins.

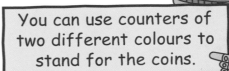

You can use counters of two different colours to stand for the coins.

- Work with a partner and take turns.
- Choose a 10p coin or a 20p coin.
  Place it anywhere on the grid.

  If you make a line of three coins that total 50p, you score 2 points.
- Carry on until all the coins are on the grid.
- Play several games.

Is it better to go first? How can you decide who starts?

Change the coins you put on the grid. Do you need to change the total?

15

Half and half

This is half a shape.

The whole shape can be any of these.

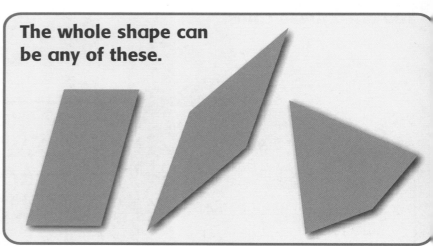

Choose your own half shape. Explore the whole shapes that can be made from your half.

Design your own half shape from card.

What if the half shape has a curved side?

Start with a shape that is a **quarter** of a whole.

UNIT 12

Choice subtractions

Use a set of 0–9 digit cards.

`0` `1` `2` `3` `4` `5` `6` `7` `8` `9`

Choose digits from the set to make subtractions and their answers.

`9` – `8` = `1`   `6` – `2` = `4`

These two subtractions leave four digit cards unused.

`0` `3` `5` `7`

Explore subtractions that leave as few cards unused as possible.

Use 2-digit numbers in your subtractions.

Don't forget to keep a record of the subtractions you make.

Start with a set of 0–20 number cards.

17

Pictogram problem

The labels are missing on this graph.

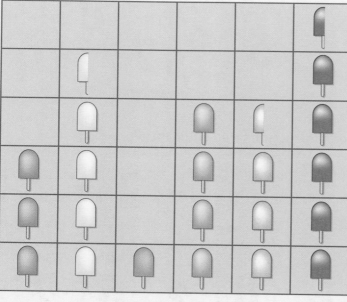

stands for …

stands for …

- What could the graph be about?
- What could the missing labels be?

Think about the different numbers each picture could stand for.

Find different solutions to these questions.

Make up some questions to ask about the graph.

18

Alphabet sums

This grid tells you what each letter is worth.

I	A	F	K	P	U	Z
2	B	G	L	Q	V	
3	C	H	M	R	W	
4	D	I	N	S	X	
5	E	J	O	T	Y	

DOG is worth 4 + 5 + 2 which is a total of 11.

Explore the totals of other animal words.

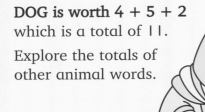

Which animal word is worth the most?

Which animal word is worth the least?

Find animal words worth every total from 10 to 20.

Find a way of sorting the animal words.

Try animal home words. Do any homes match the animal?

DOG

19

Abacus

Place 5 counters on the abacus, like this.
Make different numbers. List your numbers.

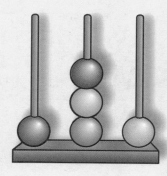

131 made using
5 counters

Look at the numbers in your list.

- Can you find pairs of numbers in your list that have a difference of 9?
- Which pair of numbers in your list has the largest difference?
- Which pair of numbers in your list has the smallest difference?

Remember to use the same number of counters for each number that you make.

Make numbers using 6 counters each time.

What if the abacus has 4 spikes?

20

UNIT 16

Number clues

39 + 3   21 + 7   23 + 19   9 + 15   3
+
5
7
+
9
5
+
3
7
+
1

Write a sum for each answer.
Use addition and odd numbers only.

Try adding more than two numbers.

Make up your own number puzzle using addition and odd numbers.

Work with a partner to make up different clues.

Make up a number puzzle that uses + and – clues.

39 + 3   43 + 25   13 + 21   27 + 11

21

Addition squares

This is how an addition square works.

3	6	
5	2	

Add each row and column.

3	6	9
5	2	7
8	8	

Find the corner total.

3	6	9
5	2	7
8	8	**16**

Try to find several solutions for each of these addition squares.

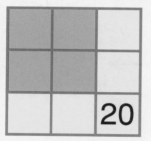

20

25

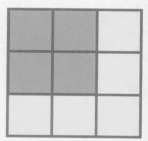

Choose your own corner total.

Can you make addition squares that use odd numbers only?

Make addition squares with a different number in each small square.

Make addition squares that have 16 small squares.

UNIT 18

Coin totals

Which totals up to 20p can you make?

Use no more than one of each coin.

Use coins if it will help you.

Some totals need lots of coins to make them.

The total 39p needs five coins.

Here is 39p.

Which totals up to £1 also need lots of coins to make them?

Record your answers in an orderly way.

Make £1 using five coins in lots of different ways.

23

Two shapes into one

How can you record the shapes you make?

Choose a pair of shapes and try to make 4-sided shapes with them.
The two shapes can be the same or different.

Explore making 4-sided shapes from different pairs of shapes.

Which pairs of shapes will make rectangles?

How many different types of 4-sided shapes can you make?

Use pair of shape to make differer 5-sided shapes.

24

Make a tocker

Make a tocker like this.

Use a lid and a small piece of Blu-tak or Plasticine.

Have a tocker race.
Whose tocker rocks longest?

What makes a tocker rock for longer?
Is it the lid or the Plasticine?

Is it the shape or the weight of Plasticine that makes a difference?

25

Twenty pence question

**The answer to a problem is 20p.
What could the problem be?**

- Find different problems where the answer is 20p.
- Find a way of sorting the problems into sets.

Sort problems into sets showing adding, subtracting, multiplying and sharing.

cost

spend

buy

sum

change

coin

price

amount

pay

value

total

cheap

sell

money

Use words in some of the problems.

Work with a partner to make up the hardest problem you can.

Target jumps

These jumps are the same size.

You must start from zero each time.

How can you land on 30?

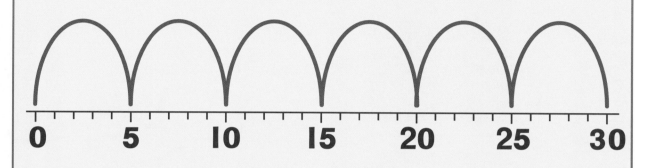

- How many jumps are there?
- How big are the jumps?

- Choose different numbers to end on.

What if you are not allowed to land on any number that has a 6 in it?

What if you have to make an odd number of jumps?

What if you start jumping from 1 instead of 0?

Domino sums

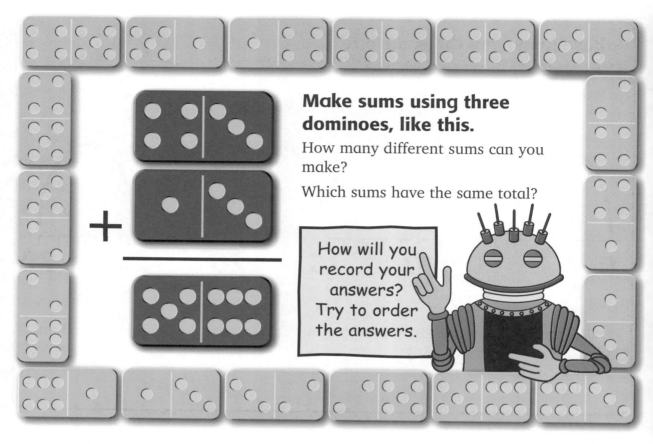

Make sums using three dominoes, like this.

How many different sums can you make?

Which sums have the same total?

How will you record your answers? Try to order the answers.

What if all the answers have to be even?

Try to arrange the whole set of dominoes into sums. Can you use all the dominoes?

Alphabet divisions

Here is a code.
Each letter of the alphabet has a number.

A	B	C	D	E	F	G	H	I	J	K	L	M
1	2	3	4	5	6	7	8	9	10	11	12	13

N	O	P	Q	R	S	T	U	V	W	X	Y	Z
14	15	16	17	18	19	20	21	22	23	24	25	26

The answers to these divisions make code words.

$$32 \div 2 \quad 27 \div 3 \quad 15 \div 3$$

$$15 \div 5 \quad 5 \div 5 \quad 55 \div 5 \quad 25 \div 5$$

What do the words have in common?

Now write some more code words to go with them.
Use division facts for the code.

Send a coded message to someone.

Make an 'odd one out' set of coded words.

Use multiplication and division facts.

29

Five-square halves

This shape is made from 5 squares.
It is half of a bigger shape.

Cut two of the shapes out of squared paper.
Explore what the whole shape could look like.

Draw the whole shapes on squared paper.
Find ways of sorting the shapes.

Start with a different arrangement of 5 squares.

What if the starting shape was a quarter of the bigger shape?

Draw a whole shape and ask your partner to find out what your half shape looks like.

30

Bar graph problem

Some labels are missing on this bar graph.

- What could the graph be about?
- What could the missing labels be?

Find different solutions to these questions.

Could the order of the columns be changed?

Make up some questions to ask about the graph.

Half past three

3:30 is the answer to a problem.

What could the problem have been?

Think about what the three hands on a clock do.

Think about timetable problems.

Think about the different ways you say and write times.

32

Breaking up

You can break up 124 in different ways.

$$124 = 100 + 20 + 4$$
$$124 = 50 + 50 + 24$$
$$124 = 70 + 50 + 4$$

Find more ways to break up 124.

Sort your results into lists.

Choose a different starting number.

Break up a 4-digit number into four parts.

Triangle totals

Corner numbers add up to the number in the middle.

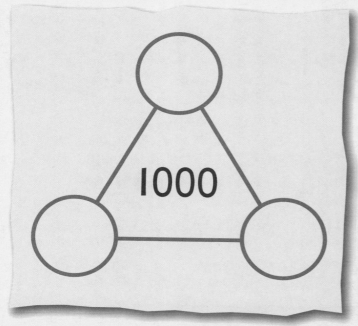

1000

Make up a rule for the corner numbers.

Find different solutions to match your rule.

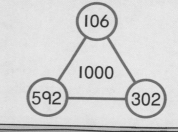

My rule is that the numbers must be **even**.

106

1000

592   302

Make up rules that include multiples.

Do some rules make solutions impossible?

Choose a different centre number.

34

Design a stamp book

Design a book of stamps worth £1.

- How many pages should be in the book?
- Which value of stamps would you have on each page?

A page does not have mixed stamps.

Think about how the stamps will be arranged on each page.

The pages of the book are the same size.

What if the book of stamps costs £5?

Corner totals

Choose rectangles and squares on the 100 grid.

1	2	3	4	5	6	7	8	9	10
11	12	13	14	15	16	17	18	19	20
21	22	23	24	25	26	27	28	29	30
31	32	33	34	35	36	37	38	39	40
41	42	43	44	45	46	47	48	49	50
51	52	53	54	55	56	57	58	59	60
61	62	63	64	65	66	67	68	69	70
71	72	73	74	75	76	77	78	79	80
81	82	83	84	85	86	87	88	89	90
91	92	93	94	95	96	97	98	99	100

Opposite corners of your shapes must total **50**, like these.

14	15	16
24	25	26
34	35	36

12	13	14	15	16	17	18
22	23	24	25	26	27	28
32	33	34	35	36	37	38

Find other rectangles with corners totalling 50.

Choose a different corner total.

Show your results on squared paper.

Start with a different number square, for example a 64 number square.

UNIT 32

Making spells

Twinkle dust 120 ml

Ninja powder 175 ml

Pink inkspots 50 ml

Jekel juice 80 ml

Shredded cobweb 125 ml

Crushed bogwort 75 ml

MAGIC SPELLS FOR GOOD

Each recipe for a magic spell to do good things must contain exactly **1 litre**.

Which bottles can be used to make a spell?

How many of each bottle are needed?

Write a recipe book for your spells.

What good things could each spell do?

What if spells must contain exactly half a litre?

Shape puzzle

Make this 3-piece shape puzzle, like this.

1 Start with a square.

2 Draw the diagonals
   lightly in pencil.

3 Cut along one diagonal.

4 Cut along the line on **one**
   of the large triangles.

○ Which shapes can you make from the two small triangles?

○ Which shapes can you make from all three triangles?

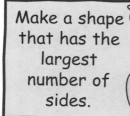

Make a shape
that has the
largest
number of
sides.

Design your
own 3-piece
shape puzzle
from a square.

Make and sort
4-sided shapes
and 5-sided
shapes.

UNIT 34

Century answers

The answer to a calculation is 100.

What could the calculation be?

Sort the calculations into sets like this.

Could there be more sets?

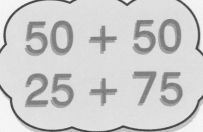

50 + 50
25 + 75

100

120 – 20
200 – 100

What could be in
the empty set?

Why not mix
up + and – in
the same
calculation?

Why not use
three numbers
in a calculation?

39

Sorting numbers

- Copy the diagram.
- Choose 3 labels from the selection and write them on your diagram.
- Choose 20 numbers for your diagram.
- A number should be in each part.

even numbers

multiples of 5

multiples of 3

less than 8

odd numbers

greater than 20

Choose a different set of labels and find new numbers to sort.

Write some labels of your own to sort numbers.

Find different ways to sort the same set of numbers.

40

UNIT 36

Puzzling remainders

Think of a number.
Divide it by 5.
The remainder is 3.
What could the
number have been?

The remainder is 4.
What could I have
divided by?

Which numbers could answer
these questions?

Is there more than one answer
to each question?

What is the
biggest remainder
you can get when
you divide by
2, 3, 4 or 5?

Which numbers
when divided
by 2, 3 and 5
do not leave
remainders?

Write remainder
questions like these
for your partner
to answer.

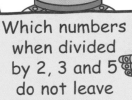

41

Matching coins

Use all of these coins.

Make matching sets that have the same totals.

Can you make four sets worth the same?

How many different matching sets can you make?

Choose a different collection of coins that is worth £1.

42

UNIT 38

Fraction shields

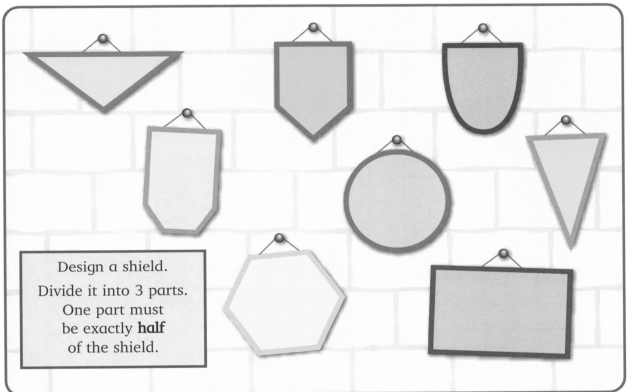

Design a shield.

Divide it into 3 parts.
One part must
be exactly **half**
of the shield.

Can you design
a symmetrical
shield?

Try different
shapes of
shields.

Divide a shield
into 5 parts.
One part must be
exactly a quarter
of the shield.

43

Measurement words

A
B
C
D
E
F
G
H
I
J
K
L
M
N
O
P
Q
R
S
T
U
V
W
X
Y
Z

Make an alphabet list.

Collect measurement words.

Try to find measurement words to go with each letter.

Why not include time words? They are used for measuring.

Which letters have no words?

Which letter has the most words?

Column graph problem

Some labels are missing from this graph.

- What could the graph be about?
- What could the missing labels be?

Find different solutions to these questions.

Could the order of the columns be changed?

Make up some questions to ask about the graph.

Decade totals

Each letter of the alphabet has a number.

A	B	C	D	E	F	G	H	I	J	K	L	M
1	2	3	4	5	6	7	8	9	10	11	12	13

N	O	P	Q	R	S	T	U	V	W	X	Y	Z
14	15	16	17	18	19	20	21	22	23	24	25	26

PIE is worth 16 + 9 + 5, which is a total of 30

30 is a **decade number**. It is part of the 10× table.

10
20
30
40
50
60
70
80
90
100

- Explore the totals of other food and drink words.

- Try to find words with totals that are decade numbers, such as 10, 20, 30, ..., 100.

How many words with decade totals can you find?

Find a word that has a decade total more than 100.

Which short word is worth the most?

Can you find a word to match each decade number?

Glossary

Difference

The difference between two numbers is how much more one is than the other.

The difference between 10 and 17 is 7.

You can find a difference by subtracting the smaller number from the larger.

Digits

There are 10 digits, 0, 1, 2, 3, 4, 5, 6, 7, 8 and 9.

Digits are used to build up other numbers.

Numbers from 10 to 99 are **two-digit** numbers.

Numbers from 100 to 999 are **three-digit** numbers.

Even numbers

These can be put into twos.

Even numbers end in 0, 2, 4, 6 or 8.

0 on its own is neither odd nor even.

Multiples

Multiples are quite like the answers to times tables.

Multiples of 2 are 2, 4, 6, 8, 10, ...

Multiples of 3 are 3, 6, 9, 12, 15, ...

Multiples of 4 are 4, 8, 12, 16, 20, ...

Multiples do not stop at the tenth one, they go on and on.

Odd numbers

These cannot be put into twos.
Odd numbers end in 1, 3, 5, 7 or 9.

Remainder

This is what is left over after dividing or sharing.

$13 \div 5 = 2$ remainder 3

Maths content

Term 1

Week 1	Unit 1	Place value
Week 2	Unit 2	Addition facts
Week 3	Unit 3	Totalling coins
Week 4	Unit 4	Estimating seconds
Week 5	Unit 5	Estimating distance
Week 6	Unit 6	Shape patterns
Week 7	Unit 7	Number facts
Week 8	Unit 8	Number sequences
Week 9	Unit 9	Place value and multiples
Week 10	Unit 10	Money game
Week 11	Unit 11	Fractions and shape
Week 12	Unit 12	Subtraction facts
Week 13	Unit 13	Missing labels on a pictogram
Week 14	Unit 14	Totalling puzzle

Term 2

Week 1	Unit 15	Place value
Week 2	Unit 16	Number facts
Week 3	Unit 17	Addition patterns
Week 4	Unit 18	Totalling coins
Week 5	Unit 19	Making quadrilaterals
Week 6	Unit 20	Practical problem on timing
Week 7	Unit 21	Money facts
Week 8	Unit 22	Sequences of multiples
Week 9	Unit 23	Addition of 2-digit numbers
Week 10	Unit 24	Division calculations
Week 11	Unit 25	Fractions, number and shape
Week 12	Unit 26	Missing labels on a bar graph
Week 13	Unit 27	Problems on a clock face

Term 3

Week 1	Unit 28	Place value and number facts
Week 2	Unit 29	Number facts
Week 3	Unit 30	Money problem
Week 4	Unit 31	Number facts and patterns
Week 5	Unit 32	Capacity problems
Week 6	Unit 33	3-piece tangrams
Week 7	Unit 34	Number facts
Week 8	Unit 35	Venn diagram and number facts
Week 9	Unit 36	Remainders
Week 10	Unit 37	Money problems
Week 11	Unit 38	Fractions of shapes
Week 12	Unit 39	General knowledge of measurement words
Week 13	Unit 40	Missing labels on a column graph
Week 14	Unit 41	Addition puzzle